USE YOUR STICKERS TO COMPLETE THE ACTIVITIES AND HELP
THE LEGO® DC SUPER HEROES COMPLETE THEIR MISSIONS.

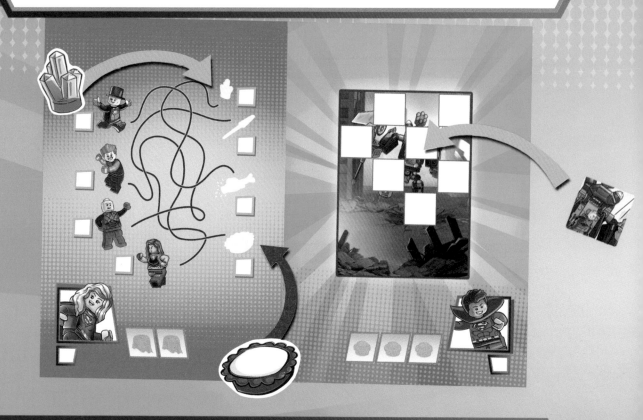

FOR EACH MISSION YOU COMPLETE, A SUPER HERO WILL REWARD YOU WITH STICKERS.
THE NUMBER OF STICKERS YOU'LL GET DEPENDS ON HOW TOUGH THE MISSION IS.

USE PENS AND PENCILS FOR MISSIONS THAT
ASK YOU TO DRAW OR COLOUR IN PICTURES.

COMPLETE THE ACTION SCENES BY PLACING YOUR
STICKERS WHERE YOU THINK THEY LOOK BEST.

WHICH JUSTICE LEAGUE SUPER HEROES ARE MISSING FROM EACH GROUP?
PLACE THE CORRECT STICKERS IN THE EMPTY SPACES.

WELL DONE! THE JUSTICE LEAGUE
IS READY FOR ACTION.

WHAT FACES DO THESE SUPER-VILLAIN MAKE IN DIFFERENT SITUATIONS? CREATE THEM WITH YOUR STICKERS!

WHEN HE'S SENT TO ARKHAM ASYLUM.

WHEN THE FLASH STOPS HER FROM ROBBING A BANK.

WHEN GREEN LANTERN FINDS HIS SECRET HIDEOUT.

YOU HAVE A TALENT FOR CREATING MEMORABLE PORTRAITS!

HELP BATMAN AND BATGIRL CATCH UP WITH THE JOKER. USE YOUR STICKERS TO CREATE A PATH THROUGH THE GRID, FOLLOWING THE PATTERN SHOWN IN THE KEY. YOU CAN ONLY MOVE VERTICALLY OR HORIZONTALLY.

YOU'RE A SKILLED NAVIGATOR. I'M IMPRESSED!

COMPLETE THE GRID WITH YOUR STICKERS SO THAT EACH SUPER HERO APPEARS ONLY ONCE IN EACH ROW AND COLUMN.

THAT WASN'T EASY!

WHO IS THE FLASH RACING? USE YOUR STICKERS TO FIND OUT!

GREAT! DO YOU WANT TO RACE US?

POISON IVY IS CUNNING. OUTSMART HER BY FINDING SIX STOLEN DIAMONDS WITHIN THE VINES AND MARKING THEM WITH ARROW STICKERS.

YOU ARE VERY PERCEPTIVE!

USE STICKERS TO COMPLETE THESE SUPER-VILLAINS'
PORTRAITS FROM THE JUSTICE LEAGUE ARCHIVE.

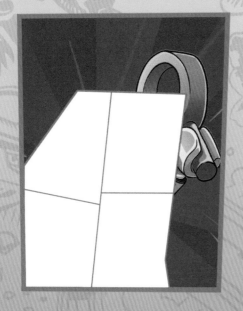

PRETTY GOOD! NOW WE KNOW WHO
TO LOOK FOR ON OUR NEXT MISSION.

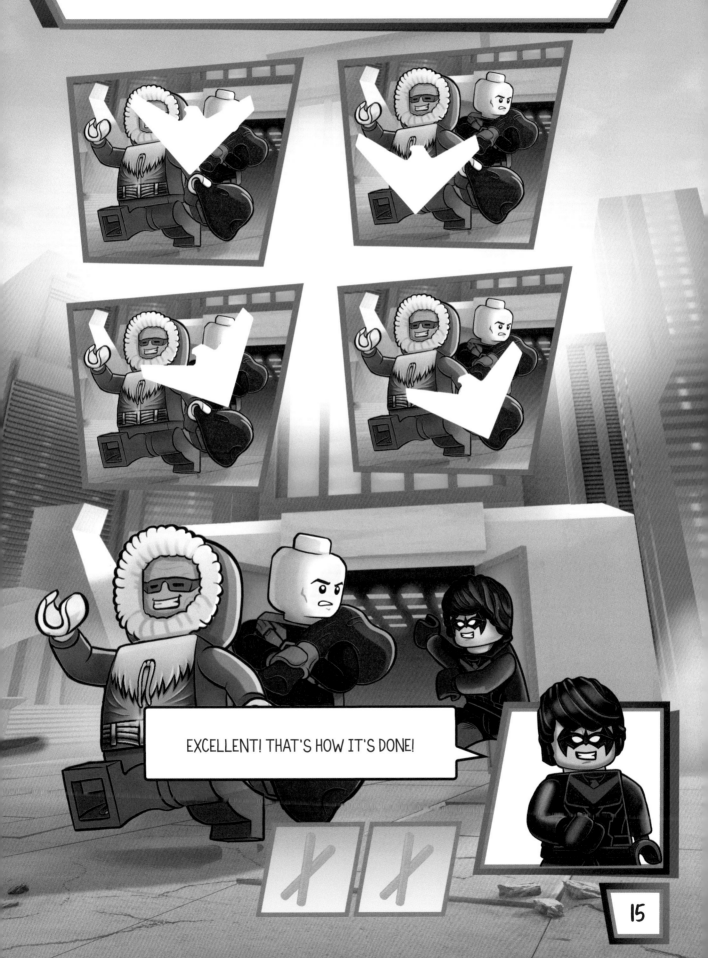

USE YOUR DRAWING SKILLS TO DESIGN A NEW MECH SUIT FOR BATMAN.

IT LOOKS GREAT! WELL DONE.

TIME TO CATCH THE RIDDLER! USE STICKERS TO MAKE WONDER WOMAN'S INVISIBLE JET APPEAR ON THE PAGE.

THAT'S WHAT I CALL A GOOD JOB! WELL DONE.

USE THE STEP-BY-STEP INSTRUCTIONS
TO COMPLETE THE DRAWING OF MAN-BAT.

WOW! YOU DIDN'T MISS A THING!

USE YOUR STICKERS TO FILL IN THE BLANK SPACES BELOW, SO THAT
THE CUT-OUT SECTIONS MATCH HOW THEY APPEAR IN THE GRID.

I WOULDN'T HAVE FIGURED
IT OUT THAT FAST!

COMPLETE THE BATCYCLE WITH YOUR STICKERS. WHEN YOU'RE DONE, PUT THE BATARANG STICKER NEXT TO THE SMALLER PICTURE THAT MATCHES THE MAIN PICTURE.

NOT BAD. NOW YOU CAN CHECK OUT MY BEAUTIFUL BATCYCLE!

DRAW ARROWS TO PUT THESE TORN PICTURE PIECES BACK TOGETHER.
ONE ARROW HAS BEEN DRAWN FOR YOU.

I KNEW YOU COULD DO IT!

ONE OF BATMAN'S BATS LOOKS DIFFERENT FROM THE OTHERS.
USE THE ARROW STICKER TO MARK IT.

CONGRATULATIONS! YOU ARE
VERY OBSERVANT!

WHAT DO YOU THINK HARLEY QUINN DREAMS ABOUT WHEN SHE'S LOCKED AWAY IN ARKHAM? DRAW IT HERE.

AWESOME DRAWING SKILLS!

MATCH YOUR STICKERS TO THE CORRECT EMPTY SPACES. WHEN YOU'RE DONE, FOLLOW THE LINES TO FIND OUT WHO EACH OBJECT BELONGS TO.

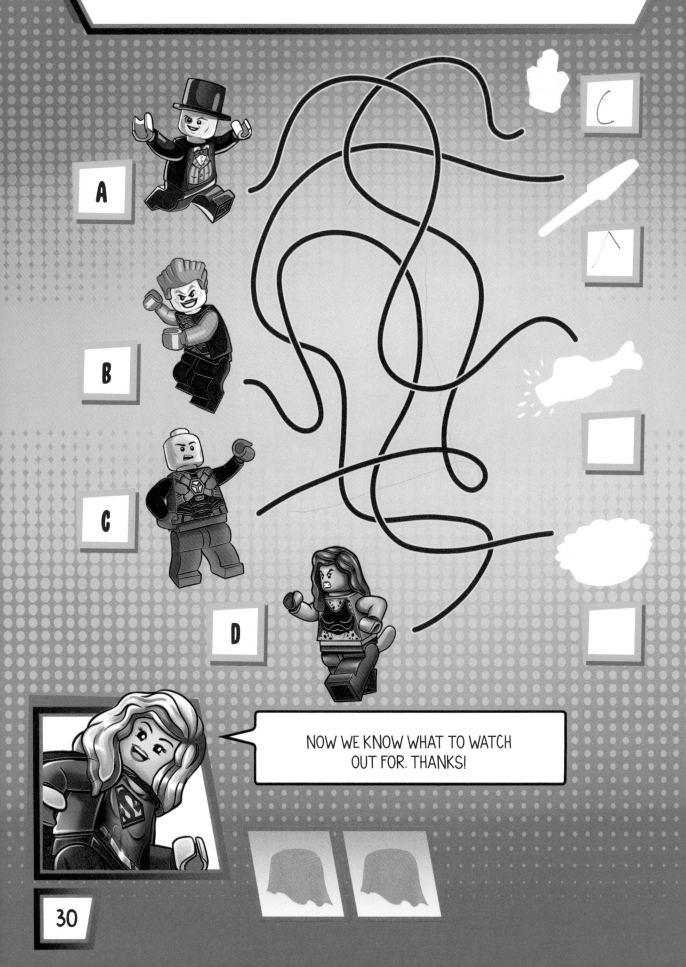

NOW WE KNOW WHAT TO WATCH OUT FOR. THANKS!

ADD YOUR STICKERS TO THE CORRECT SPACES TO REVEAL
SUPERMAN'S CLASH WITH LEX LUTHOR.

GOOD WORK!

FIND THE STICKERS FOR THESE THREE PARTS, THEN USE THE ARROW STICKER TO POINT TO THE VEHICLE THEY COME FROM.

GROOVY! NOW BATMAN AND I ARE READY TO ROLL.

SUPER HEROES ALWAYS LOOK IMPRESSIVE! MATCH THE CLOSE-UP STICKERS TO THE SUPER HEROES THEY COME FROM.

WOW, THEY ALL LOOK AMAZING!

THE RIDDLER IS FLEEING FROM A ROBBERY! USE YOUR STICKERS
TO ADD EVEN MORE ACTION TO THIS SCENE.

GREAT! TIME TO CLEAN UP!

USE YOUR STICKERS TO COMPLETE THIS SCENE. WHEN YOU'RE DONE, USE THE ARROW STICKERS TO POINT TO EACH PLACE WHERE THE SMALL PICTURES DIFFER FROM THE BIG ONE.

1

2

3

NOT BAD!

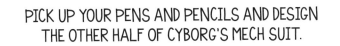

PICK UP YOUR PENS AND PENCILS AND DESIGN
THE OTHER HALF OF CYBORG'S MECH SUIT.

I LIKE IT! TIME TO TAKE
IT OUT ON A MISSION.

37

COMPLETE THE BATMOBILE WITH YOUR STICKERS, THEN USE A PEN TO MARK THE PIECE IN EACH GROUP THAT MATCHES THE SPOT WHERE THE ARROW POINTS TO. ONE HAS BEEN MARKED FOR YOU.

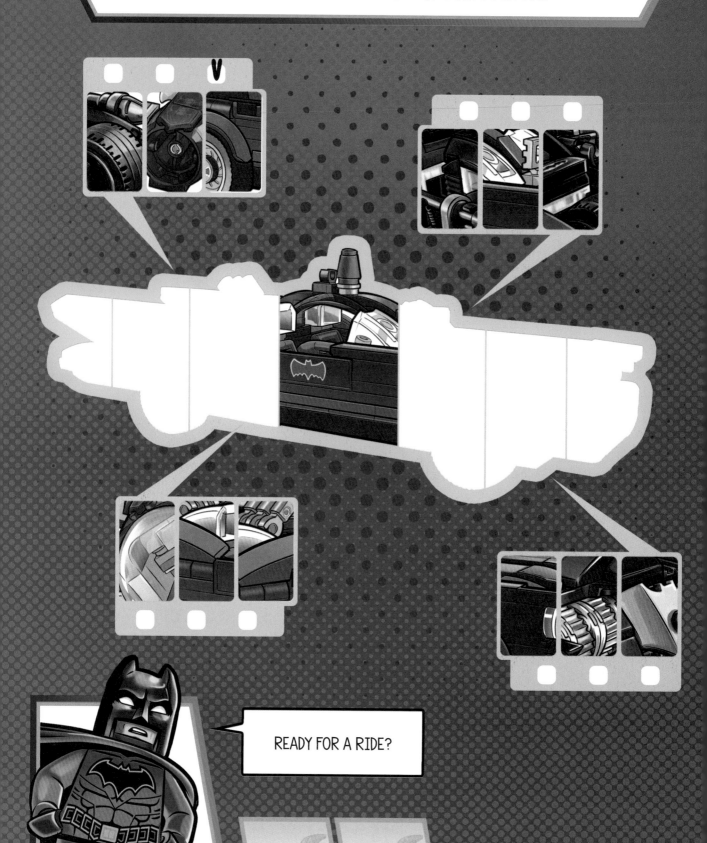

READY FOR A RIDE?

STICK THE SUPER-VILLAINS' PORTRAITS ON THEIR SHADOWS. THE ONE WHO ONLY APPEARS ONCE JUST ROBBED THE BANK! TAG THE CULPRIT WITH A MONEY STICKER.

THAT WASN'T SO EASY.
THANKS!

BUILD GREEN LANTERN'S SPACESHIP WITH YOUR STICKERS.
WHEN YOU'RE DONE, USE THE RING STICKER TO MARK THE ONE
SHADOW THAT PERFECTLY MATCHES THE SPACESHIP.

WELL DONE. YOU SHOULD BE
PROUD OF YOURSELF!

STICK BRAINIAC'S PICTURE IN THE SPACE BELOW AND THEN USE YOUR ARROW STICKER TO POINT TO THE ONE TRUE PHOTO OF HIM.

WITH YOUR SUPPORT, WE'RE SURE TO CATCH BRAINIAC!

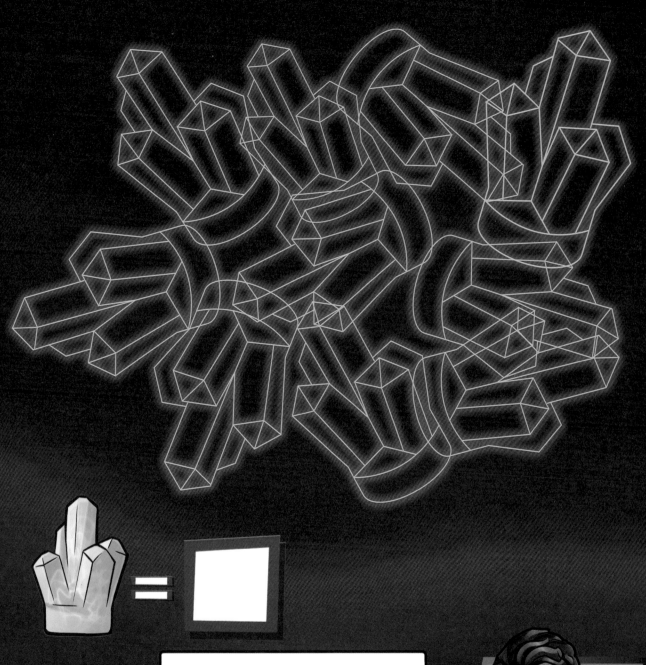

I'D BETTER BE CAREFUL!

FANTASTIC JOB! WE STAND TOGETHER!

CREATE LOBO'S SPACE HOG BIKE WITH YOUR STICKERS. WHEN YOU'RE DONE, USE THE ARROW STICKER TO POINT TO THE CLOSE-UP TAKEN FROM THE VEHICLE.

YOU DID WELL. IT'S TIME TO FACE LOBO!

THANKS FOR THE BACKUP!

LOOK AT THESE PHOTOS AND DRAW A CIRCLE AROUND
THE SUPER-VILLAIN THAT IS MISSING FROM EACH ONE.

YOUR INSIGHT IS VERY USEFUL!

48

USE YOUR ARROW STICKER TO MARK WHICH OF THESE SMALL PICTURES MATCHES THE BIG PICTURE OF KILLER CROC.

PERFECT!

THERE'S SO MUCH ACTION RIGHT NOW! COMPLETE THE PICTURE USING THE CORRECT STICKERS, THEN ADD AN ARROW STICKER TO MARK THE PARTS THAT ARE IN THE PICTURE.

  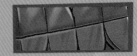

THANKS! TIME TO GET IN ON THE ACTION!

UNTANGLE THE LINES TO FIND OUT WHO IS CALLING FOR BATMAN'S HELP.

NICE WORK. NOW I KNOW WHO NEEDS MY SUPPORT!

# WHICH CARD LOOKS EXACTLY LIKE THE ONE THE JOKER IS HOLDING? MARK IT WITH AN ARROW STICKER.

YOU DID WELL. KEEP IT UP!

BATMAN IS IN HOT PURSUIT! USE YOUR STICKERS TO FIND OUT WHO HE IS AFTER.

I NEVER DOUBTED YOU!

FILL IN THE BLANKS WITH STICKERS, THEN HELP THE FLASH
REACH GORILLA GRODD AS FAST AS POSSIBLE.

WE'LL NAB THIS SUPER-VILLAIN
IN NO TIME!

THERE'S A MISTAKE IN EACH OF THE SMALLER PICTURES OF BATMAN.
FIND AND MARK EACH ONE WITH AN ARROW STICKER.

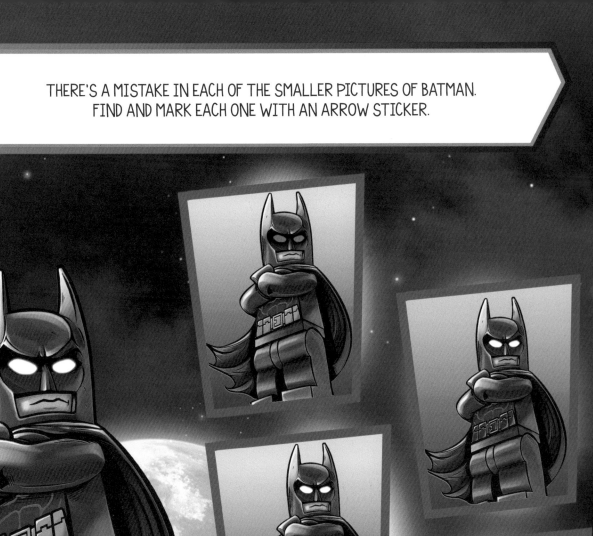

YOU FOUND THEM ALL. CONGRATULATIONS!

HOW MANY SHARKS ARE SWIMMING AROUND AQUAMAN? COUNT THEM AND DRAW A CIRCLE AROUND THE CORRECT NUMBER.

7

9

8

THANKS FOR THE USEFUL INFO!

USE LEAF STICKERS TO MARK WHICH CLOSE-UPS ARE FROM
THE PICTURE OF POISON IVY'S MECH SUIT.

YOU FIGURED THAT OUT FAST!

BATMAN IS VENTURING INTO THE DEEP!
USE YOUR STICKERS TO REVEAL HIS BATSUB.

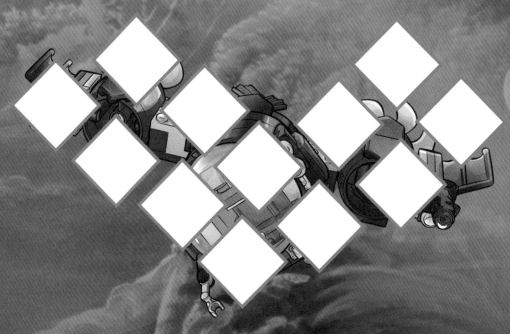

WELL DONE. I'LL BE JOINING
BATMAN SOON!

LOOK AT THE SMALL COMBINATIONS OF SUPER-VILLAINS ON THE RIGHT. CAN YOU FIND EACH OF THEM IN THE GRID?

AWESOME! YOU DID IT!

FILL IN THE SHAPES WITH THE CORRECT STICKERS, THEN FIND
THE ONE THAT DOESN'T APPEAR IN THE PICTURE.

THAT WAS EASY AS PIE FOR YOU!

YOU DID THAT IN NO TIME!

USE YOUR STICKERS TO FIND OUT WHO AQUAMAN HAS DISCOVERED IN THE DEPTHS.

YOU DID GREAT! WOW!

# ANSWERS

# ANSWERS

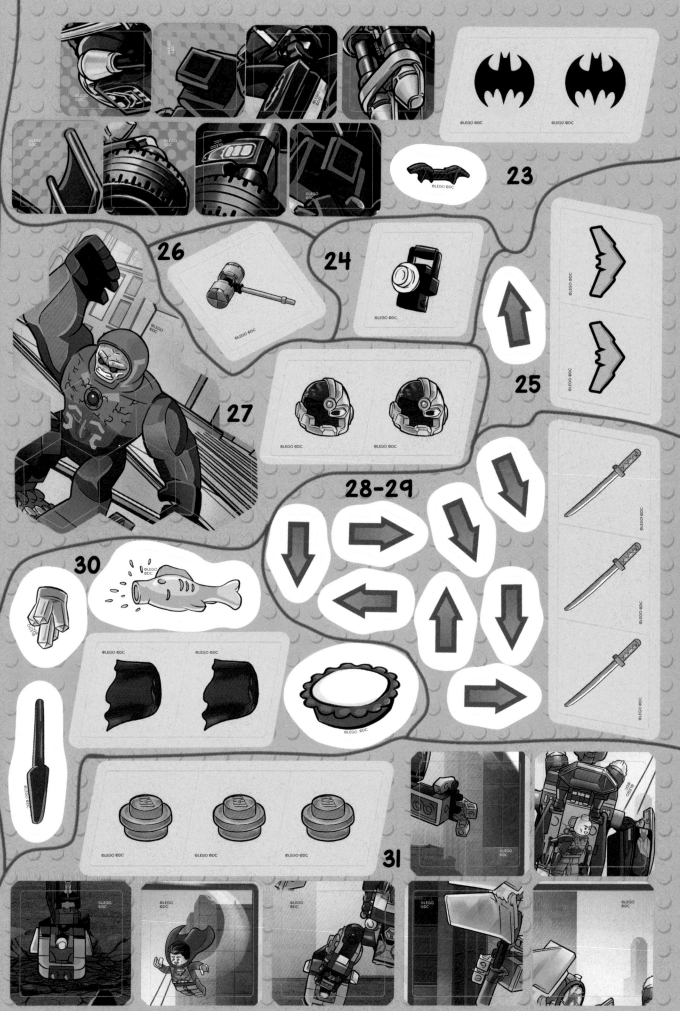

23

26

24

25

27

28-29

30

31

32

33

34-35

36

37

38

38

39

40

41

42

43

44

45

46-47

48    50

49

51

52

53

53

54

55

56

57

58

59

60

61

62